CREATIVE STRATEGIES

A Self-Guided Journal to Help You Kick Depression

PAMELA SHAKIR, MSW, LCSW

Largo, MD

Christian Living Books, Inc.
P. O. Box 7584
Largo, MD 20792
christianlivingbooks.com
We bring your dreams to fruition.

ISBN 9781562295332

CONTENTS

Introduction   5

Step 1 – Understand the Issues   7

Step 2 – Make Affirmations   13

Step 3 – Use Positive Reflection Strategies   21

Step 4 – Set Goals   73

Step 5 – Free Your Mind   87

Mental Health Crisis Resources   111

Dedication   113

Acknowledgments   115

About the Author   116

Endnotes   118

INTRODUCTION

I am delighted you decided to pick up this coping journal to help you kick depression, which is a heavy burden in your life. You feel alone, isolated, sad, and just tired of pushing to get out of the same old despondent place. The kicker is you do not even know why you have these feelings. If this is not your story, although it sounds familiar, maybe it is the reality of a sister, brother, child, family member, coworker, or a dear friend.

Depression is real, and it can be deadly if not dealt with properly. I have heard people say, "I feel so depressed" and oftentimes, they don't know why. Despite overwhelming feelings of sadness, worry, hurt, and grief caused by divorce, financial strain, relationships gone bad, and other life issues, they do not seek help. As a result, they struggle to function.

We have many reasons for continuing to live with depression rather than getting help. I don't know your reason, but I hope his coping journal will help you unpack your feelings, deal with your emotions, and break the stigma. You do not have to suffer in silence. Your mind and heart deserve to heal.

Depression is a common disorder that prevents people from moving forward with their lives in freedom and wholeness. The mind and heart must be in sync to function harmoniously. And this journal will help you get that done. As you dive purposefully into it and do the work, you will see positive and meaningful outcomes in your life.

I encourage you to apply this journal to your daily life and picture yourself in a better place where you are joyful and healed. Faith is an essential element that drives you forward when depression works hard to keep you dormant, sad, and tired. Anytime you attempt to move your mind and heart, it will take work and a lot of effort. Crucially, it also takes a made-up mind. I often tell people when you are ready to live freely and boldly, then you are truly ready to heal.

Life has a way of changing at a moment's notice causing you to stay broken. Nevertheless, you can rise like a phoenix from the ashes when you allow coaching and positive reinforcements in your life. It helps you to recover from what you might call catastrophic life events.

Allow me to encourage you to do the work necessary to see yourself in a healthier, better place. Now and then, it's worth pausing to just chill and reflect on what has helped you to stand strong on your journey to recovery. Healing and wholeness are your destinations.

STEP 1

UNDERSTAND THE ISSUES

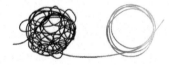

According to Google, depression is "characterized by persistent sadness and a lack of interest or pleasure in previously rewarding or enjoyable activities."

Mayo Clinic defines depression this way:

> Depression is a mood disorder that causes a persistent feeling of sadness and loss of interest. Also called a major depressive disorder or clinical depression, it affects how you feel, think, and behave and can lead to a variety of emotional and physical problems. You may have trouble doing normal day-to-day activities, and

sometimes you may feel as if life isn't worth living. More than just about the blues, depression isn't a weakness, and you can't simply "snap out" of it. Depression may require long-term treatment. But don't get discouraged. Most people with depression feel better with medication, psychotherapy, or both.[1]

Can you relate? Is this you? Have you been diagnosed? Would you like to gain more knowledge to help someone?

Objective

My objective is to help you maneuver through depression and develop healthy habits for a better life. This journaling process will assist you in discovering your self-worth and help you relocate to a healthy place mentally and emotionally. First, I want you to realize you are valuable and then actively take the necessary steps to conquer depression. I challenge you to do the work to get the best results and set yourself free.

The Goal

Do the work. Be consistent in your journaling process. Be honest and tell your truth.

The End Goal

To heal from the inside out.

Patient Health Questionnaire-9 (PHQ-9)

Over the last 2 weeks, how often have you been bothered by any of the following problems? *(Use "✔" to indicate your answer)*	Not at all	Several days	More than half the days	Nearly every day
1. Little interest or pleasure in doing things	0	1	2	3
2. Feeling down, depressed, or hopeless	0	1	2	3
3. Trouble falling or staying asleep, or sleeping too much	0	1	2	3
4. Feeling tired or having little energy	0	1	2	3
5. Poor appetite or overeating	0	1	2	3
6. Feeling bad about yourself — or that you are a failure or have let yourself or your family down	0	1	2	3
7. Trouble concentrating on things, such as reading the newspaper or watching television	0	1	2	3
8. Moving or speaking so slowly that other people could have noticed? Or the opposite — being so fidgety or restless that you have been moving around a lot more than usual	0	1	2	3
9. Thoughts that you would be better off dead or of hurting yourself in some way	0	1	2	3

FOR OFFICE CODING ___0___ + _____ + _____ + _____

=Total Score: _____

If you checked off any problems, how difficult have these problems made it for you to do your work, take care of things at home, or get along with other people?

Not difficult at all	Somewhat difficult	Very difficult	Extremely difficult
☐	☐	☐	☐

Developed by Drs. Robert L. Spitzer, Janet B.W. Williams, Kurt Kroenke and colleagues, with an educational grant from Pfizer Inc. No permission required to reproduce, translate, display or distribute.

[Source – American Psychological Association[2]]

CREATIVE STRATEGIES

Scoring Directions

Below are the scores for each box checked. Add up each box you checked to get your total score.

Not at all = 0

Several days = 1

More than half the days = 2

Nearly every day = 3

Score Results

The scores indicated provide you with an understanding of where you range on the depression questionnaire scale.

1 – 4 = Minimal depression

5 – 9 = Mild depression

10 – 14 = Moderate depression

15 – 19 = Moderate Severe depression

20 – 27 = Severe depression

Please seek the help of a mental health professional if you have scored in the range of mild and above.

"You may encounter many defeats, but you must not be defeated. In fact, it may be necessary to encounter the defeats, so you can know who you are, what you can rise from, how you can still come out of it."

— Dr. Maya Angelou[3]

STEP

2

MAKE AFFIRMATIONS

Affirmations are powerful reminders of the inner strength you possess when life's disappointments cloud your thinking. Affirmations also help you to see the good in you. I have included five positive affirmations that will help you make meaningful changes in your life as you repeat and believe them. However, these are only to get you started. I challenge you to create and write down your own and speak them over your life daily. You can also post them on your wall or mirror. Remember I am cheering for you.

Five Positive Affirmations to Get You Going

1. I release pain and say hello to loving myself.

2. I choose peace over chaotic negativity.

3. Happiness minus sadness equals freedom in my mind.

4. I have total control over my emotions and actions.

5. I welcome healthy and positive thoughts.

Create your own affirmations and write them in the spaces provided below.

I Am... _____

_____

_____

_____

_____

_____

_____

_____

_____

_____

I Am...

I Can...

_____

_____

_____

_____

_____

_____

_____

_____

_____

_____

_____

_____

_____

_____

_____

_____

_____

_____

CREATIVE STRATEGIES

I Can...

I Will..._____

_____

_____

_____

_____

_____

_____

_____

_____

_____

_____

_____

_____

_____

_____

_____

CREATIVE STRATEGIES

I Will..._____

_____

_____

_____

_____

_____

_____

_____

_____

_____

_____

_____

_____

_____

_____

_____

_____

_____

_____

_____

3

USE POSITIVE REFLECTION STRATEGIES

Journaling is one strategy used to heal. In the section below, take a moment to reflect and write down how you feel about yourself. Be honest about it. Writing things down brings clarity to our thoughts. The objective is to fill this entire section with thoughts of yourself to increase self-awareness. In doing so, you will acquire a better understanding of your feelings and behaviors.

Why are you thankful or hopeful? Give specific reasons. Block out all the negative expressions in your mind and write all positive thoughts.

_____

_____

_____

_____

_____

_____

_____

_____

_____

_____

_____

_____

_____

_____

_____

_____

_____

_____

_____

_____

_____

_____

_____

_____

_____

_____

_____

_____

_____

_____

_____

_____

_____

_____

_____

REFLECTION 2

What is your definition of being healed? What would your life look like if it is healed?

_____

_____

_____

_____

_____

_____

_____

_____

_____

_____

_____

_____

_____

_____

CREATIVE STRATEGIES

_____

_____

_____

_____

_____

_____

_____

_____

_____

_____

_____

_____

_____

_____

_____

_____

_____

_____

Depression can be triggered by various situations and events, for example, job loss, marital and other relationship issues. Distractions can also be triggers. What distractions do you encounter that keep you from being healed?

_____

_____

_____

_____

_____

_____

_____

_____

_____

_____

_____

_____

_____

_____

_____

_____

_____

_____

_____

_____

_____

_____

_____

_____

_____

_____

_____

_____

_____

_____

_____

_____

_____

What is one thing in your life you would change if you could? Why?

_____

_____

_____

_____

_____

_____

_____

_____

_____

_____

_____

_____

_____

_____

_____

_____

_____

_____

_____

_____

_____

_____

_____

_____

_____

_____

_____

_____

_____

_____

_____

_____

_____

_____

_____

_____

REFLECTION 5

How do you perceive depression and what effects does it have on you?

_____

_____

_____

_____

_____

_____

_____

_____

_____

_____

_____

_____

_____

_____

_____

_____

_____

CREATIVE STRATEGIES

_____

_____

_____

_____

_____

_____

_____

_____

_____

_____

_____

_____

_____

_____

_____

_____

_____

_____

_____

Let's pause and take a moment to breathe. Inhale positive thoughts. Exhale negative thoughts. Keep going. You're doing a good job. Now, let's continue your healing journey. I am with you every step of the way. I am cheering for you.

Thank you so much for your responses thus far. In the following section, you will discover further strategies in the coping skills I have put in place for you to live a better life and heal completely. Be healed. Be whole.

STRATEGY 1 - HEAL

To heal is to become healthy again. Write a letter of encouragement to your future self. Only include positivity, no negative responses.

_____

_____

_____

_____

_____

_____

_____

_____

_____

_____

_____

_____

_____

_____

_____

_____

_____

_____

_____

_____

_____

_____

_____

_____

_____

_____

_____

_____

_____

_____

_____

STRATEGY 2 – BE YOU

Be who you truly want to be. Why is this difficult for many people?
How can you be yourself and be free?

_____

_____

_____

_____

_____

_____

_____

_____

_____

_____

_____

_____

_____

_____

CREATIVE STRATEGIES

_____

_____

_____

_____

_____

_____

_____

_____

_____

_____

_____

_____

_____

_____

_____

_____

_____

_____

_____

_____

Take lots of pictures. Pick out the best 5 photos of yourself. After looking at them, write down how you feel inside.

_____

_____

_____

_____

_____

_____

_____

_____

_____

_____

_____

_____

_____

_____

_____

_____

_____

_____

_____

_____

_____

_____

_____

_____

_____

_____

_____

_____

_____

_____

_____

_____

_____

_____

_____

_____

_____

_____

_____

What exactly does your exercise routine consist of? Give an example of how exercising makes you feel. Has it helped you?

What challenges do you encounter when trying to stay motivated to exercise?

_____

_____

_____

_____

_____

_____

_____

_____

_____

_____

_____

_____

_____

_____

_____

_____

_____

_____

_____

_____

_____

_____

_____

_____

_____

_____

_____

_____

_____

_____

_____

_____

_____

_____

_____

_____

_____

_____

_____

When was the last time you smiled? What made you smile?

_____

_____

_____

_____

_____

_____

_____

_____

_____

_____

_____

_____

_____

_____

_____

_____

_____

_____

_____

_____

_____

_____

_____

_____

_____

_____

_____

_____

_____

_____

_____

_____

_____

_____

_____

_____

STRATEGY 6 – LAUGH AND LAUGH AND LAUGH

Do absolutely nothing here but write in bold letters I WILL LAUGH, LAUGH, and LAUGH again.

_____

_____

_____

_____

_____

_____

_____

_____

_____

_____

_____

_____

_____

_____

_____

_____

_____

_____

_____

_____

_____

_____

_____

_____

_____

_____

_____

_____

_____

_____

_____

_____

_____

STRATEGY 7 – DEEP BREATHING EXERCISES

Inhale for 4 seconds.

Hold your breath for 7 seconds.

Exhale for 8 seconds.

Journal how this particular exercise made you feel. Try this daily. Revisit this question and make notes of your progress.

_____

_____

_____

_____

_____

_____

_____

_____

_____

_____

_____

_____

_____

CREATIVE STRATEGIES

_____

_____

_____

_____

_____

_____

_____

_____

_____

_____

_____

_____

_____

_____

_____

_____

_____

_____

_____

STRATEGY 8 - WATCH YOUR FAVORITE MOVIE

Quite often we learn a great deal from meaningful movies.

Journal why this movie is your favorite. What did you learn and what were your 5 takeaways from the movie?

_____

_____

_____

_____

_____

_____

_____

_____

_____

_____

_____

_____

_____

_____

_____

_____

_____

_____

_____

_____

_____

_____

Forgiveness is not for the other person; forgiveness is for you. What and who do you need to release? Why have you held on to stuff for so long? Go deep and write down why unforgiveness has invaded your life. What does it mean to forgive?

_____

_____

_____

_____

_____

_____

_____

_____

_____

_____

_____

_____

_____

_____

_____

_____

_____

_____

_____

_____

_____

_____

_____

_____

_____

_____

_____

_____

_____

_____

_____

_____

STRATEGY 10 - READ

Escape by reading your favorite novel.

Place yourself in a book. What would your book title be? Write a short introduction. Take a moment and escape by rewriting your story for a better outcome.

_____

_____

_____

_____

_____

_____

_____

_____

_____

_____

_____

_____

_____

_____

_____

_____

_____

_____

_____

_____

_____

_____

_____

_____

_____

_____

_____

_____

_____

_____

_____

_____

_____

It's time to be creative. Creativity is a superpower that can change the trajectory of your life. Following is a list of coping skills. Select 7 areas and write 7 strategies from the list below.

Coping Skills

[ ] Journal your thoughts daily

[ ] Attend a paint night

[ ] Call or FaceTime friend(s)

[ ] Surround yourself with like-minded people

[ ] Go out to your favorite place to eat

[ ] Meditate daily

[ ] Get a massage

[ ] Listen to upbeat music

[ ] Write down what you are grateful for

[ ] Do random acts of kindness

[ ] Take a nap

[ ] Go to a concert

[ ] Go on a hike

[ ] Dance, dance, and dance

[ ] Travel

[ ] Think Positive

_____

_____

_____

_____

_____

_____

_____

_____

_____

_____

_____

_____

_____

_____

_____

_____

_____

_____

_____

_____

_____

COPING SKILL 2

_____

_____

_____

_____

_____

_____

_____

_____

_____

_____

_____

_____

_____

_____

_____

_____

_____

_____

_____

_____

CREATIVE STRATEGIES

_____

_____

_____

_____

_____

_____

_____

_____

_____

_____

_____

_____

_____

_____

_____

_____

_____

_____

_____

COPING SKILL 4

_____

_____

_____

_____

_____

_____

_____

_____

_____

_____

_____

_____

_____

_____

_____

_____

_____

_____

_____

_____

_____

CREATIVE STRATEGIES

_____

_____

_____

_____

_____

_____

_____

_____

_____

_____

_____

_____

_____

_____

_____

_____

_____

_____

_____

_____

_____

_____

_____

_____

_____

_____

_____

_____

_____

_____

_____

_____

_____

_____

_____

_____

_____

_____

_____

_____

_____

_____

_____

_____

_____

_____

_____

_____

_____

_____

_____

_____

_____

_____

_____

_____

_____

_____

_____

_____

_____

IT'S YOUR MOMENT
TO CREATE.

BE ORIGINAL!

Creativity Strategy 1

Use the following pages to create your own strategies. Just do you!

_____

_____

_____

_____

_____

_____

_____

_____

_____

_____

_____

_____

_____

_____

_____

_____

_____

Creativity Strategy 2

_____

_____

_____

_____

_____

_____

_____

_____

_____

_____

_____

_____

_____

_____

_____

_____

_____

_____

_____

_____

Creativity Strategy 3

Creativity Strategy 4

_____

_____

_____

_____

_____

_____

_____

_____

_____

_____

_____

_____

_____

_____

_____

_____

_____

Creativity Strategy 5

Creativity Strategy 6

_____

_____

_____

_____

_____

_____

_____

_____

_____

_____

_____

_____

_____

_____

_____

_____

_____

_____

Creativity Strategy 7

_____

_____

_____

_____

_____

_____

_____

_____

_____

_____

_____

_____

_____

_____

_____

_____

_____

_____

_____

CREATIVE STRATEGIES

30-Day Self-Care Calendar

DAY 1	DAY 2	DAY 3	DAY 4	DAY 5
Unplug from social media	Do your make-up	Drink water	Read an inspiring book	Take a bubble bath

DAY 6	DAY 7	DAY 8	DAY 9	DAY 10
Take moments to sit quietly	Do a little shopping	Listen to a positive podcast	Write out your goals	Binge watch a movie series

DAY 11	DAY 12	DAY 13	DAY 14	DAY 15
Rest	Get a facial	Turn your phone off	Get a pedicure	Dress up today

DAY 16	DAY 17	DAY 18	DAY 19	DAY 20
Do your hair	Take a walk	Eat a healthy meal	Decline invites	Maintain healthy boundaries

DAY 21	DAY 22	DAY 23	DAY 24	DAY 25
Get a manicure	Write the vision for your life	Complete a task	Organize your closet	Listen to music

DAY 26	DAY 27	DAY 28	DAY 29	DAY 30
Take yourself out on a date	Practice self-love	Do a hobby	Pat yourself on the back	Put yourself first

STEP

SET GOALS

One of the main ways to be hopeful instead of depressed is to work toward fulfilling your dreams. For your dreams to be realized, you must turn them into steps and actions—goals.

What are your dreams? Be specific. Know what you want. You have a specific purpose on the earth. You are on the earth to do something amazing with your life. While all humans have certain, general things in common, there is also something unique, distinct, and specific about you. You will never realize more than a fraction of your potential as a wandering generality. I like how Zig Ziglar aptly stated it many years ago,

"You must become a meaningful specific and not a wandering generality." It is a fact that people who have direction and purpose in their lives go further and faster. They get more done in all areas of their lives.

A goal is what you want to achieve in a given amount of time. What makes a goal valid is taking it out of the realm of generality and making it specific. What makes it specific is the time limit you put on it. A goal is your anticipated result. It's an end you strive to attain, toward which your effort and energy are directed. When your goals are time-framed, it suggests the end is in view. Since time limits render a goal concrete, let us look at the classifications of goals to give us a better perspective:

Long Term: 10–25 Years

A long-term goal is something you want to achieve in the long run, better known as the future. Long-term goals are important for a successful life and career. A long-term goal is not something you can do this week or even this year. Rather, it is a life-achievement goal—your main focus and what you want to be remembered for. That is why long-term goals usually take ten to twenty years to achieve; sometimes, they can take even longer. Again, it is not something you can finish in one day, one week, one year, or even five years. It is the big picture or the grand scheme of your life. It will take many steps to complete a long-term goal. These smaller steps are your short-term and medium-term goals.

Medium Term: 5–10 Years

A medium-term goal is a springboard upon which you can leap to your long-term goals. It is the bridge for the achievement of your long-term goals. The medium term goals are usually longer

CREATIVE STRATEGIES

than one year but will not go beyond ten years. They are typically met between five and ten years. Medium-term goals are the leverage goals upon which you can build your life. Therefore, you must always keep an eye on them, making sure you are moving in the right direction and at the right pace.

Short Term: 1–5 Years

Experts have stated a short-term goal is something that takes at least a year to accomplish. Short-term goals can range between one and five years. These are the foundational goals that will enable the completion of the medium to long-term goals. Small things make the difference. It is what you want to happen in the near future. You must keep in mind that just as a building can be no stronger than its foundation, your long-term goals will not be met without the achievement of short-term goals.

Immediate Term: Daily/Weekly/Monthly

This is what gets the ball rolling. Without immediate or pressing goals, you are procrastinating. It is what you do, daily, that will determine what you experience in five, ten, and twenty years. Achieving pressing goals will enable you to reach your short-term goals. In turn, it will give you the ability to achieve your medium terms goals, which will empower and strengthen you to complete your long-term goals. You need to work on your daily goals to set the infrastructure to achieve your long-term goals. To complete the big picture, you must start somewhere. Start with the here and now goals.

Be SMART

What are the most important criteria that make "goals" viable? Set realistic goals. Having an unrealistic goal is like trying to get to the moon without a spaceship. It is just not going to happen! This is where we have to apply the SMART goal principle. The SMART goal principle will expose what an unrealistic goal is. You need to fully grasp this concept. SMART is an acronym:

S Specific

M Measurable

A Attainable

R Realistic

T Time-Bound

S Specific

Set specific goals—nothing vague, broad, or general. Vague goals create vague results. Know exactly what you are shooting for. A goal that is well-defined will give clarity, direction, and focus. The moment you focus on a goal, it becomes like a magnet, pulling you and the necessary resources toward it. A specific goal will answer the following six questions:

1. Who will be the personnel involved? Your goals will need assistance.

2. What exactly do you want to accomplish?

3. Where is this happening? Identify a location. Placement and positioning are extremely important.

4. When will this happen? Establish a time frame. If you do not, you will flounder in procrastination and delaying tactics.

5. Which requirements and constraints are in play? Which skills do I need? What don't I have? Which habits do I need to implement in my life? Which people do I need to walk away from?

6. Why am I doing this? What are the specific reasons for

7. accomplishing the goal?

M Measurable

Some goals are easy to measure such as weight loss or income; others are a bit more difficult. Being able to track progress is an incentive to push further. You need to establish concrete criteria for measuring progress. A goal without a measurable mechanism or conclusion is like playing sports without a scoreboard or scorekeeper.

A Attainable

Stretch for it! You will not attain what you do not strive for. Your goal will need to stretch you—not break you. It will demand you are action-oriented. Action gives traction.

R Realistic

An unrealistic goal is an unreachable goal. By realistic, I mean the goal must be relevant and real to you. A realistic goal is one toward which you are willing and able to work and commit to. Some people set unreasonably lofty goals. Even as they are setting them, in their minds, they know they will not be able to fulfill the obligations. That does not mean you should set low goals. A goal can be both high and realistic. You are the determining factor on whether your goal is realistic or unrealistic, high or low.

T Time-Based

There must be a deadline. This is what separates a goal from a mere wish. Time-bound goals will be the difference between success and mediocrity in your life. Putting a deadline—a finish line or an expiration date—on a particular goal gives you a clear target to work toward. When there is no time frame, there will be no sense of urgency. Procrastination will be the order of the day. A time-bound goal is what will eliminate procrastination and time wasting.

The SMART goal principle will teach you how to set goals correctly and keep you on track for their successful execution.

[Source: *Turning Your Dreams into Realities*[4]]

PERSONAL GOAL

START DATE: **ACHIEVE BY:**

Describe Your Personal Goal   **Progress Check**

_____

_____

_____

_____

Actionable Steps   **Reason for This Goal**

☐ _____

☐ _____

☐ _____

☐ _____

☐ _____

Challenges   **Notes** _____

_____

_____

_____

_____

_____

_____

RELATIONSHIP GOAL

START DATE:　　　　　　　　**ACHIEVE BY:**

Describe Your Relationship Goal　**Progress Check**

_____
_____
_____
_____
_____

Actionable Steps　　　　**Reason for This Goal**

☐ _____
☐ _____
☐ _____
☐ _____
☐ _____

Challenges　　　　**Notes** _____

_____
_____
_____
_____
_____
_____

CAREER GOAL

START DATE:

ACHIEVE BY:

Describe Your Career Goal

_____
_____
_____
_____
_____

Progress Check

Actionable Steps

☐
☐
☐
☐
☐

Reason for This Goal

_____
_____
_____
_____
_____

Challenges

Notes _____
_____
_____
_____
_____
_____
_____

CREATIVE STRATEGIES

SPIRITUAL GOAL

START DATE: **ACHIEVE BY:**

Describe Your Spiritual Goal

_____

_____

_____

_____

Progress Check

Actionable Steps

- [ ]
- [ ]
- [ ]
- [ ]
- [ ]

Reason for This Goal

_____

_____

_____

_____

_____

Challenges

Notes _____

_____

_____

_____

_____

_____

_____

HEALTH & FITNESS GOAL

START DATE: **ACHIEVE BY:**

Describe Your Health & Fitness Goal   Progress Check

_____

_____

_____

_____

_____

Actionable Steps   **Reason for This Goal**

[ ]   _____

[ ]   _____

[ ]   _____

[ ]   _____

[ ]   _____

Challenges   **Notes** _____

_____

_____

_____

_____

_____

_____

FINANCIAL GOAL

START DATE: **ACHIEVE BY:**

Describe Your Financial Goal

_____
_____
_____
_____
_____

Progress Check

Actionable Steps

☐
☐
☐
☐
☐

Reason for This Goal

_____
_____
_____
_____
_____

Challenges

Notes _____

_____
_____
_____
_____
_____
_____

SOCIAL GOAL

START DATE:　　　　　　　　**ACHIEVE BY:**

Describe Your Social Goal

_____
_____
_____
_____

Progress Check

Actionable Steps

- [ ]
- [ ]
- [ ]
- [ ]
- [ ]

Reason for This Goal

_____
_____
_____
_____
_____

Challenges

Notes _____
_____
_____
_____
_____
_____
_____

STEP

5

FREE YOUR MIND

Congratulations! You have done an excellent job creating your affirmations, self-reflection, setting goals, and your own strategies for healing. You have learned a lot about yourself during this journaling experience. Now you have done the work in this coping journal, get up and continue to fight until you have the life you deserve and want. Will you have some days that are not easy? Yes, you will, but keep pushing until you conquer depression.

Remember the creative strategies you wrote down. Use and apply them to your life daily. You have what it takes inside of you to be your absolute best. We will end with a space that allows you to do you. Use this space in whatever way is best for you. Whether you draw, doodle, write poetry, reflect, create a diary, or set some strategic goals, remember, I am cheering for you.

Free Your Mind...

Free Your Mind...

Free Your Mind...

Free Your Mind...

Free Your Mind...

Free Your Mind...

Free Your Mind...

Free Your Mind...

Free Your Mind...

CREATIVE STRATEGIES

Free Your Mind...

Free Your Mind...

MENTAL HEALTH CRISIS RESOURCES

National Suicide Prevention Lifeline

1-800-273-8255

Free and confidential support 24 hours a day, 7 days a week for prevention, people in distress and/or in crisis.

National Alliance on Mental Illness (NAMI) Helpline

1-800-950-NAMI (6264)

Monday-Friday from 10am-10pm EST

info@nami.org

Crisis Text Line

Text HOME to 741741

Free 24 hours a day, 7 days a week support to anyone in crisis.

National Sexual Assault Hotline

1-800-656- HOPE (4673)

Free and confidential support 24 hours a day, 7 days a week.

National Domestic Violence Support Hotline

1-800-799- SAFE (7233)

For confidential and anonymous support 24 hours a day, 7 days a week

National Human Trafficking Hotline

1-888-373-7888

Text: 233733

For confidential and anonymous support 24 hours a day, 7 days a week.

If you or a loved one is currently experiencing a crisis, seek help immediately. If you or a loved one is experiencing a medical or mental health emergency call 911.

DEDICATION

To my mother, Debra, who we all affectionately call "grandma," Mom, it all began with you and my dad, Lonnie; when you both decided to bring me into this world. Who would have thought I would be the first author in our family? You both are special to me and I thank you dearly for being my parents.

To my sister, Alicia, you are my hero. You inspire me more than you know. You faced some major challenges, but God has kept you here with us. I am happy you are here to see this moment come true. I thank God for you and for your selfless love. I love you dearly.

To my beautiful, kind and loving daughters, Courtney, Lyric and Sa'Miah who I call my "sweetie loves," I thank God for you every day. You have inspired me to dream big and to go after all my dreams. You are my "why." I pray that you all live in the true purpose of what God has called you to do on this earth. To my grandchildren, Kyren, Kylin and Nyeli. My heart is so full because of you. I love you all more than you can imagine.

ACKNOWLEDGMENTS

To my spiritual leaders, I treasure all of the endless support, guidance and love you have shown me throughout the years. First Lady Vicki, you've taught me how to walk in love, how to support other women, and how to go after my dreams. You reminded me of a conversation we had many years ago when I told you I wanted to write a journal. The seed was planted, but you pushed me to water the seed. I thank you so much for your unconditional love. I pray that God continues to bless all of you beyond your imagination.

To my sisters, Patrinia Redd, Patricia Roland, Jenene Shears, Kimberly Fleming, Niesha Davis, Patricia Perry, and Matasha Level, most of you have been my sisters since the sandbox. I feel so honored to have you all in my life. Each of you has a special place in my heart. Continue to thrive, be bold, and live out your dreams. Don't be afraid. Just do it. I'm cheering for you.

To Niesha, I owe you a special thank you. I thank you for allowing me to first start my journey as a therapist at Life Connections. You brought me in and taught me how to run a private practice business. I truly appreciate what you did for me. You are a true gem.

To my entire family, there is nothing you can't do if you put your mind to it. Take one step and keep walking. To my brother, Craig, your memory will forever be sketched in my heart. To my siblings, Alicia, Lennean, Todd and Mark, I'm forever grateful to be your little sister. Thank you for being the example of true love.

ABOUT THE AUTHOR

Pamela Shakir is a Licensed Clinical Social Worker and Owner and CEO of Healing Minds and Hearts, LLC, a psychotherapy provider. She is a therapist, consultant, and mental health advocate who has worked with children and families for over 25 years. She has also worked in the fields of child welfare, corrections and rehabilitation, healthcare, and education and currently serves as a Clinical Therapist for a school district in the Atlanta, Georgia area.

Pamela has a Master's in Counseling and Social Work from California State University, Bakersfield. She specializes in working with women and couples who struggle with communication concerns, relationship trauma, and disagreements within their relationships. Strategically, Pamela has worked with adolescents, adults, and families who struggle with loss, depression, anxiety, rejection, substance abuse, and life transitions. She enjoys speaking to women about women's issues, ways to improve their coping skills, and how to heal from trauma. Pamela formerly served as a School Social Worker, advisor for Young Women Empowered for Leadership, committee member and presenter for Project Next Step at Kern High School District in Bakersfield, CA.

She has three beautiful and intelligent daughters: Courtney, Lyric, and Sa'miah and resides in Atlanta, GA.

Connect with the Author

⊙ pamelashakirlcsw

◉ pamelashakirlcsw.com

f Healing Minds and Hearts, LLC

ENDNOTES

1   "Depression (Major Depressive Disorder)." Patient Care and Health Information. Mayo Foundation for Medical Education and Research, February 3, 2018. https://www.mayoclinic.org/diseases-conditions/depression/symptoms-causes/syc-20356007.

2   Gilbody, S., J. B. Williams, R. L. Spitzer, K. Kroenke, C. Hewitt, S. Brealey, and D. Richards, D. "Patient Health Questionnaire (PHQ-9 & PHQ-2)." American Psychological Association, June 2020. https://www.apa.org/pi/about/publications/caregivers/practice-settings/assessment/tools/patient-health.

3   *Pocket Maya Angelou Wisdom: Inspirational Quotes and Wise Words from a Legendary Icon.* Hardie Grant Books, 2019.

4   Arekion, Glenn. *Turning Your Dreams into Realities.* Largo, MD: Christian Living Books, Inc., 2015.

Made in the USA
Columbia, SC
02 November 2021